This Journal Belongs To :